THE TROJANS

ENGLISH VERSIONS OF OPERA LIBRETTI

THE ABDUCTION FROM THE SERAGLIO

ABU HASSAN

UN BALLO IN MASCHERA

THE BARBER OF SEVILLE

BEATRICE AND BENEDICK

BENVENUTO CELLINI

DR. MIRACLE

DON GIOVANNI

DON PASQUALE

L'ELISIR D'AMORE

EUGENE ONEGIN

FIDELIO

FRA DIAVOLO

DER FREISCHÜTZ

THE MAGIC FLUTE

THE MARRIAGE OF FIGARO

MARTHA

ORPHEUS

THE QUEEN OF SPADES

RIGOLETTO

LA TRAVIATA

THE TROJANS

IL TROVATORE

THE TROJANS

OPERA IN FIVE ACTS
AND TWO PARTS

The Capture of Troy
and
The Trojans at Carthage

Words and Music by
HECTOR BERLIOZ

English Version by
EDWARD J. DENT

LONDON
OXFORD UNIVERSITY PRESS
NEW YORK   TORONTO

Oxford University Press, Ely House, London W.1

GLASGOW NEW YORK TORONTO MELBOURNE WELLINGTON
CAPE TOWN SALISBURY IBADAN NAIROBI LUSAKA ADDIS ABABA
BOMBAY CALCUTTA MADRAS KARACHI LAHORE DACCA
KUALA LUMPUR SINGAPORE HONG KONG TOKYO

NOTE

First Edition 1957
Reprinted 1957, 1966, *and* 1969

SET IN GREAT BRITAIN BY
JARROLD AND SONS LTD., NORWICH
AND REPRINTED LITHOGRAPHICALLY BY
HALSTAN AND CO. LTD., AMERSHAM.

PREFACE

WHEN the first of all operas was produced at Florence towards the end of the sixteenth century (the date is uncertain) the book of words was printed (in 1600) probably as a souvenir to be given away to the noble ladies and gentlemen who had been invited to the performance, and ever since then it has been the custom to print the words of operas as little books—hence the international name for it, *libretto*, a little book. The first librettos were written by real poets; in fact the words were often better than the music. As long as operas were composed mainly for the cultivated classes, librettos maintained a reasonably high standard, in whatever language they were written. Quinault wrote in French for Lully, Dryden for Purcell in the seventeenth century; in Italy Apostolo Zeno and Metastasio carried on the tradition of literary dignity into the eighteenth. That century, too, is the great age of comic opera, with admirable humorists such as Goldoni, Bickerstaffe, Sedaine, and Casti—the Gilbert of his day —to say nothing of Mozart's friend Da Ponte. It was not until the days of Verdi—from about 1840 onwards— that the word *libretto* became a byword for nonsense and doggerel. Verdi's audiences were noisy and ill-educated; they wanted roaring melodrama (the word *melodramma* is the classical Italian word for *opera*, which about 1650 was still rather colloquial), with music that could be taken up for political purposes. No wonder that there are still nice-minded people who say they prefer their operas in a language they do not understand.

Opera in English dates back to 1656, but after the

death of Purcell in 1695 it languished. Italian opera was established as a fashionable entertainment, and opera in English was only what we should call 'musical comedy'. Out of this comic opera grew what in the nineteenth century was known as 'grand romantic opera'; and its English landmarks were Weber's *Oberon*, written for London, 1826, and the English performances of Beethoven's *Fidelio* (with Malibran as the heroine) in 1833. But it is difficult to translate bad Italian into anything but worse English, and the result has been that opera in English is to most people a lamentably ridiculous affair. Opera in English will never flourish until a tradition of really good translation is established. Far be it from me to speak ill of my predecessors: Thomas Oliphant's version of *Fidelio* (1833) is a model of good style. Unfortunately it sounds too elegant for the present day; owing to changes in literary convention, translations, like accompaniments to folk-songs, must sooner or later become out of date, and have to be rewritten.

English is a perfectly good language for singing, if singers will take the trouble to pronounce it naturally, as actors do. Even when English is difficult to sing, it is less difficult than German can be in some of the standard German operas. The first duty of a translator is to make the story of the opera clear, and to write words simple enough to be intelligible when sung. If only for this reason, the words must be accurately fitted to the music; and after all these conditions are fulfilled, there is not much chance left for 'poetry'. The reader is asked to remember that the words of these English versions have been written to be sung and acted, not to be read. Stage scenery is not meant to be hung in a private house; the scene-painter is satisfied if it looks reasonably well on the stage. If the reader discovers in these pages any line that he can call poetry, he may be sure that it has been stolen from some more respectable—and, I hope, non-copyright —author.

E. J. D.

INTRODUCTION

HECTOR BERLIOZ (1803–1869), although we are now within a few years of the centenary of his death, is still a composer whose reputation, especially in the field of opera, is a matter of vigorous dispute. At the height of his fame, about a hundred years ago, he was associated mainly with the pioneers of what was called the Music of the Future, with Liszt and Wagner, but we must remember that he was actually older than either of those two and that in some ways he belonged to an earlier generation. The Romantic movement in France is generally said to date from Victor Hugo in 1830; Berlioz's passion for the colossal style goes back to the previous century and the musical conceptions of his teacher Le Sueur, who was much interested in the revival of the ancient Greek modes. Le Sueur is often said to have brought the music of the theatre into the church and that of the church into the theatre; he belonged to the group of composers who planned the grandiose musical celebrations of the French Revolution and the years that followed it into the age of Napoleon. When Berlioz, the son of a country doctor, decided to throw up his medical studies and devote himself entirely to music, his first musical enthusiasms were the operas of Gluck and the symphonies of Beethoven, then new to Parisian audiences: then came the operas of Spontini and the first performances in Paris of Weber's *Der Freischütz*. We must remember the grossly mutilated form in which they were first presented to Parisian audiences. But Paris was the musical centre of Europe to which all the leaders of modern music were naturally attracted, and Berlioz, who matured early, came into close personal contact with them. He did not neglect, as has often been supposed, either his medical or his musical studies, although he was obliged to earn a living by journalism and by singing in the chorus of minor theatres. At the Opéra and the Opéra Comique he had no success; his first opera, *Benvenuto Cellini*, intended as a comic opera, was produced at last in 1838 at the Opéra in two acts only, against an organized opposition. It was revived at Weimar by Liszt in 1852 and again in 1856 in a very clever translation by Peter Cornelius. Berlioz himself conducted it (in an Italian version) at Covent Garden in 1853; its first performance in English was at Glasgow under Dr. Erik Chisholm.

After the failure of Paris in 1838 Berlioz gave up opera as hopeless until after the encouragement in Germany under Liszt and Hans von Bülow. His return to the stage was due mainly to the persuasions of Princess Sayn-Wittgenstein, who lived with Liszt at Weimar for several years. She was not very musical herself, but wished to keep Liszt away from the influence of Wagner.

Berlioz had begun to read Virgil with his father about the time that Wagner was in his cradle, and ever since he had first been moved to tears by the story of Dido and her desertion by Aeneas he had been a devoted student of the Roman poet. He began to sketch the libretto of *The Trojans* in 1856 and finished the composition of the music, including the completion of the whole score, in 1861.

In his earlier days Wagner certainly learned a good deal from Berlioz; it may have been the example of Wagner that induced Berlioz to write the poem of *The Trojans* himself, and to treat it as an epic, the history of a nation rather than a drama of individual characters. The tale of Dido had been treated by various older librettists, but there is no reason to suppose that Berlioz was acquainted with any of them. It is obvious that he worked direct on the original Latin of the *Aeneid* (Books II and IV) and his words are often a close translation; the opera is dedicated to Virgil himself—DIVO VIRGILIO. For this English version the translator has made use, wherever possible, of Dryden's translation. The other literary enthusiasm of Berlioz was Shakespeare; he fell violently in love with the Irish actress Harriet Smithson, who appeared in Paris with an English company in 1827, taking the parts of Ophelia and Juliet.

STORY OF THE OPERA

Berlioz had intended that his work should be given complete, but his publisher insisted on dividing it into two parts, the first of which is dominated by Cassandra, who has the gift of prophesying the future; she foretells the truth, but no one will believe her. After besieging Troy for ten years, the Greeks have unexpectedly retired; the Trojans leave their walls and we see them enjoying their liberty. Cassandra, aloof from the crowd, is joined by Choroebus, a Trojan warrior to whom she is betrothed; he persuades her to join her father and mother at a ceremony of thanksgiving, while the crowd rush off to see the wooden horse which the Greeks have left behind. Priam and Hecuba preside over the ceremony. Andromache, widow of Hector (silent part) enters with her little son Astyanax and presents him to the King and Queen; the crowd express their subdued sympathy but Cassandra, always apart from the rest, warns them of disaster to come.

Aeneas enters in haste to tell the King that Laocoon, the chief priest of Neptune, has been strangled by two serpents which came out of the sea after he had thrown a javelin at the horse, suspecting some treachery of the Greeks. After an ensemble of horror, Priam orders that the horse shall be brought into Troy by a breach in the wall, since it is too large to pass the gate, and deposited in the temple as an offering to Pallas. The procession of the whole people has already started, although for a moment it is halted by the noise of clashing arms within it. Cassandra, always alone, watches in prophetic agony as night falls and the horse is brought into the city to the sound of the Trojan March which is the symbolic theme of the whole opera.

The next scene is the tent of Aeneas. The ghost of Hector appears to him and warns him to save what he can and sail with the survivors to the shores of Italy where he is to be the founder of a great and glorious empire. In the last scene we see the women of Troy gathered together in the temple of Cybele. Cassandra warns them of the doom to come; the Greek soldiers enter and are astonished to see the Trojan women singing their hymn to the goddess and finally committing suicide.

The second part of the opera shows us Dido receiving the homage of the people of Carthage. (Here Berlioz obviously remembered the opening of the Great Exhibition of 1851 by Queen Victoria; he had been present himself as one of the jury invited to report on the musical instruments, as he describes in *Les Soirées de l'Orchestre*, and the chorus in praise of Dido was obviously suggested by our own National Anthem.)

The arrival of Aeneas and the Trojans is announced and Dido offers them a generous welcome. Aeneas is disguised as a common sailor, and the presentation of gifts is made by his young son Ascanius. Narbal, the Queen's first minister, tells her that Carthage is being attacked by a savage horde of Numidians. Aeneas throws off his disguise and leads the Trojans and Carthaginians to battle. The Numidians are defeated, but Anna and Narbal are much concerned at Dido's change of mind. She neglects the cares of state and is obviously in love with Aeneas, all the more since he has told her that Andromache has married again. This is the scene of the great septet, followed by the duet taken from the scene between Jessica and Lorenzo in *The Merchant of Venice*. Mercury suddenly appears and reminds Aeneas of his duty to sail for Italy.

The next scene is that of the royal hunt and storm, modelled to a great extent on the scene of the Wolf's Glen in *Der Freischütz*. The next scene shows the harbour, beginning with the song of the young Trojan sailor Hylas. There is an amusing dialogue between two Trojan soldiers who have no wish to leave the comforts and amusements of Carthage. Aeneas warns the Trojan chieftains that they must sail at once; ghosts of Hector, Cassandra, and others repeat their warnings. Dido is heart-broken and reproaches Aeneas, but he is now determined to leave her. In the final scene she calls on the priests of Pluto, curses Aeneas and foretells the vengeance of Hannibal; but her last vision is that of Eternal Rome.

*   *   *

First performance, Paris, Théâtre Lyrique, 4 November 1863, much cut, with a prologue taken from the first part. The complete opera was first performed at Karlsruhe under Felix Mottl, translated into German by Otto Neitzel, 6 and 7 December 1890; subsequent German performances at Munich. Various arrangements of the opera were given in Germany after

1890; a French arrangement at Brussels, 1906, Rouen 1920, Paris (Opéra) 1921, and both parts were performed at Glasgow under Dr Erik Chisholm, 18 and 19 March 1935. This was the first performance in English and the first performance of this English version. Reduced arrangements at Birmingham (1948) and Oxford (in French, 1950).

THE CAPTURE OF TROY
OPERA IN THREE ACTS

CHARACTERS
(in the order of their appearance)

A TROJAN SOLDIER	*Baritone*
CASSANDRA, daughter of Priam	*Soprano*
CHOROEBUS, betrothed to Cassandra	*Baritone*
ANDROMACHE, widow of Hector	—
ASTYANAX, her son	—
AENEAS	*Tenor*
HELENUS, son of Priam	*Tenor*
ASCANIUS, son of Aeneas	*Soprano*
HECUBA, wife of Priam	*Mezzo-soprano*
PANTHEUS, a Trojan priest	*Bass*
PRIAM, King of Troy	*Bass*
THE GHOST OF HECTOR	*Bass*
POLYXENA, daughter of Priam	*Soprano*
A GREEK CHIEFTAIN	*Bass*

Trojan People, Trojan Soldiers, Greek Soldiers.

SCENE. *Troy, at the end of the siege.*

ACT I

SCENE. *A wooded part of the plain of Troy. At one side there is a throne, at the other, a rustic altar, with the grave of Achilles. Three shepherds are playing the flute, sitting on the tomb. The people of Troy, with Trojan soldiers, are spread over the plain, rejoicing, and dancing.*

PEOPLE. What delight to breathe again
The sweet fresh air!
Ten years besieged behind our walls we waited,
While in rage unabated
They assail'd us in vain.
The Greeks are gone, their army has departed,
Troy now is free once more;
For the battle is over and the victory won.

Women and children look at the remains of arms on the ground.

Look what is here!
A Grecian helmet!
And here's a sword!
In such haste did they flee!
This mighty shield some hero left behind him
Should serve him for a boat to sail the sea!
Greeks are cowards, I say!

A TROJAN SOLDIER. Do you know whose the tent was
That stood just here, here on the spot?

PEOPLE. Whose? Can you say? Whose tent?

SOLD. The tent of Achilles.

PEOPLE. Ah!

SOLD.   Fear not, he cannot harm you,
          For he is dead.
          Within this tomb his bones are buried.
          Here he lies.

          The flute-players flee in terror. The people draw back.
          The soldier goes away with a smile of contempt.

PEOPLE.   Indeed 'tis true,
          And that slaught'rer of Trojans,
          By Paris he was slain.
          But have you seen the wooden horse
          Which, ere they departed for Aulis,
          The Greeks built and left here?
          An immense wooden horse
          They have made as an off'ring to Pallas.
          In its entrails an army might be lodg'd.
          'Twill be carried to the temple
          Through a breach in the walls;
          It cannot pass the gate. The King, they say,
          The King himself is coming soon.
          Where stands it now?
          On the banks of Scamander.
          Then let us haste to view this wonder!
          So come, come all! To the horse, to the horse!

          The people rush out in tumult. Before the end of this
          scene CASSANDRA *has entered among the groups,*
          traversing the plain with wild and agitated looks.

CASS.   The Greeks have quit the plain;
          Yet what may be the cause?
          Why in such sudden haste
          Have all at once departed?
          Dark thoughts assail my heart
          With presage of disaster!

Last night on the walls of Troy
I mark'd a watchman stride—
The ghost of Hector!
His eyes gaz'd out afar
Beyond the plain to seaward,
To the straits of Sigeium—
Alas! And Troy rejoices in wild exultation,
Her gates flung open wide;
Priam the King, my father, leads the way.

Unhappy King! Down to eternal night,
I see thee fall, thy reign is ended!
Oh, wherefore were my words by thee uncom-
    prehended?
Unhappy Priam! Unhappy Troy!
Now thy last hour has come.
Choroebus too, he so dearly that loves me,
Thinks me bereft of reason!
When I think upon him, I tremble.
Oh, Choroebus! He loves me, I love him!
Yet we shall ne'er be wed,
Never hear the sweet hymn of Hymen,
Our dream of love is past for ever.
Dreadful is the doom that awaits us,
The doom of Fate's inexorable law!

> *She falls into a tender reverie.*

Choroebus!
And I could save him, would he but believe me!

Enter CHOROEBUS *in haste from the back of the scene.*

He comes!

CHOR.   All Troy exulteth in triumph and joy;
Why do you fly the festive throng?
Like some nymph of the woods

3

You seek a place of silence.
The King sends me to find you.

CASS. Ah, I dare not reveal
The horrid fear that my soul overwhelmeth.

CHOR. Cassandra!

CASS. Nay, begone!

CHOR. Come!

CASS. Leave me, I beseech thee!

CHOR. Thou dost bid me begone?
Thou, whom in wedlock holy—

CASS. 'Tis the hour of our death,
And of love 'tis the end.

CHOR. Belovèd heart, cease thy sad repining,
Calm thy distress and thy wild prophetic strain,
Raise thine eyes to heav'n brightly shining,
Read its fair vision with glance divining,
Bid farewell to grief and pain,
Trust in love, and hope again.

CASS. No hope has heav'n for me.
Believe my word: inspir'd am I
By that same fell god Apollo,
Who to destroy us is resolv'd.
His hand has touch'd my eyes:
I foresee all the future,
I read the book of Fate,
I behold the doom of Troy.

(*With restrained but ever increasing exaltation.*)

Yes, Troy shall be no more,
Disaster on us falls,
I see the vision clear.

Our streets run red with blood,
Fire rages in our halls,
I see the holy virgins
Dragg'd naked from their fane,
I hear their terrible cries,
They call to the goddess in vain.
I see the vultures black
Upon each lofty tower,
They are crying and calling,
Doom appalling!
Troy falling!
Naught remains but a wrack
And in thy heart a Grecian sword!
Ah!

CASSANDRA *falls half swooning into the arms of* CHOROEBUS.

CHOR.   Unhappy Cassandra!
Belovèd heart, cease thy sad repining, etc.

CASS.   I behold Death range the air,
I behold the lightning's flare,
Herald of the storm that shall destroy us!
If thou lov'st me, begone! fly!
Go back to thy father,
Think of him in his last declining years,
Think no more upon me.

CHOR.   And if I went, what would my father say
To me, his son? Dearest Cassandra,
If I were base enough to flee,
And leave thee, my betrothèd,
In dire danger and dread?

All is peace around us,
War and bloodshed forgotten,

No danger need thou fear.
Hear the breeze's balmy whisper,
Hither borne across the water.
Hark to the sea-wave soft lapping,
Message of hope and peace,
Wouldst thou but only hear!
On the billowy pasture
Graze contented the herds,
A shepherd sings his roundelay,
Echo'd by happy birds,
Heav'n gratefully adoring
In song that ne'er may cease,
Ev'ry voice is outpouring
One sweet anthem of peace.

CASS.   Thou art deceiv'd; false hope deludes thee,
For I behold Death range the air,
I behold the lightning's flare,
Herald of the storm that shall destroy us!

Leave me, leave Troy this night,
Hear my words, I implore thee,
Death stands waiting before thee.
Go, ere dawn brings the light!
Death is near us, I say,
Look not on me with wonder,
When my heart's torn asunder.
Oh, begone ere the day!

CHOR.   Leave thee, leave thee tonight?
Cassandra, I adore thee,
Tell me not, I implore thee,
I must fly from thy sight!
Thou my heart tear'st asunder.
Dost thou bid me fly thee,

6

        Oh, belovèd Cassandra,
        No, near thee I would stay!

CASS.   By all the love that thou hast borne me
        I do beseech thee now to fly from here.

CHOR.   By all gods, or in heav'n or in Hades,
        Cassandra, now lend me thine ear.
        Here at thy knees a suppliant,
        Here at thy knees I make my prayer,
        Cassandra!

CASS.   How can I resist thy tears of anguish?
        O cruel gods!
        Blind as the rest art thou.
        Wilt thou persist too
        To sacrifice thyself for thy disastrous love?

CHOR.   I will not leave thy side.

CASS.   And on that dreadful dawn
        Thou with thy brothers wilt meet thy death in
           battle?

CHOR.   I will not quit thy side.

CASS.   Choroebus! Then take my hand,
        And my virgin kiss seal our betrothal!
        Stay now, and Death shall escort us;
        By her hand is the bride-bed prepar'd,
        For tonight!

CHOR.   Come, come!

                        He takes her away distraught.

END OF ACT I

ACT II

SCENE. *Before the citadel. A throne on the left, an altar on the right.*
Enter PRIAM, HECUBA, HELENUS *and* POLYXENA
with the other sons and daughters of PRIAM; AENEAS
at the head of the Trojan soldiers, ASCANIUS *leading
the children; Magistrates, Priests of Neptune and
Jupiter followed by the people.* PRIAM *and* HECUBA
*take their seats on the throne. A procession is made
round the altar. Various groups deposit on it offerings
of flowers, wine, honey, lambs, doves, etc.*

PEOPLE. Almighty gods through whom Troy stands eternal,
Take our thanks and our incense receive,
As from our hearts to your dwelling supernal
Grateful prayer we upheave.

Enter ASCANIUS *at the head of the children.*

Ye gods, whose gracious will
Has wrought us our salvation,
Lord of Olympus, hear our prayer,
Lord of the waters, bend thine ear!
Ye who guide all in earth and heaven,
Take these offerings we bear
In thankful adoration.

Enter HECUBA *and the Princesses.*

Lord of Olympus, etc.

Enter AENEAS *and warriors.*

Almighty gods, etc.

Enter PRIAM *and the Priests.*
Dance of wrestlers.

ANDROMACHE *enters slowly, holding* ASTYANAX *by
the hand. Both are dressed in mourning (white).*

8

PEOPLE. Andromache and her son!
Cruel fate!
In the midst of all our public rejoicing!

ASTYANAX lays a basket of flowers at the altar;
ANDROMACHE kneels for a few moments in prayer.

She comes in sorrow and mourning,
In grief and woe, in silence and tears!

She rises and leads her son to PRIAM, *presents him to*
the King and Queen and then embraces him with con-
vulsive tenderness.

Every wife, every mother
Weeps at so sad a sight.

PRIAM blesses ASTYANAX, HECUBA *does the same.*
They sit down again on their thrones. ASTYANAX
shyly returns to his mother, who shows increasing grief
and emotion. CASSANDRA *passes behind.*

CASS. Andromache! Waste not thy tears,
Hector is dead. Disaster yet to come
Will soon call for tears in abundance!

ANDROMACHE takes ASTYANAX *by the hand and*
passes between the groups of people to the back.
Several Trojan women weep, hiding their faces on the
shoulders of the men near them. ANDROMACHE *and*
ASTYANAX *go out slowly.*

AENEAS comes forward in haste.

AEN. O King, behold me here in haste to bring you
A tale of horror, a tale of dread!
Fear has seiz'd ev'ry heart;
So appalling a portent was ne'er seen till now.
Our holy priest, Laocoon,
Some ambush suspecting in this horse of the
    Greeks,

9

Seiz'd a javelin and hurl'd it
At the monster, transfixing its flank,
And the people then did incite
To consign the horse to the flames.
And then, O sight of horror!
From the sea two serpents came
Across the plain advancing,
Made straight for Laocoon and clasp'd him,
Round his waist and his throat entwining,
And their fiery crests on high uplifting,
Upon his face their fell poison outpouring,
They devour'd him before our eyes!

AENEAS. HELENUS *and* CHOROEBUS.

At a doom so appalling
Fear ev'ry heart must seize!
Wrath of the gods on us is falling
And makes our ev'ry vein to freeze!
Throes of awful dread invade us;
What gods dare we pray to aid us?
Chastisement falls upon us;
What sins may have undone us?

(*The other characters repeat the same words.*)

PEOPLE. Ye gods!
All my blood in each vein is a-freeze.
Fear and dread our hearts are now invading.

ALL. Laocoon, of all men!
The priest, the holy priest of God!
By the serpents devour'd
As at Neptune's altar he stood,
Thus a victim he fell!

AEN. May holy Pallas now protect us!
We must seek to appease her wrath.

The sign is hers; 'tis she who thus
On sacrilege wreaketh her vengeance.

PRIAM.　We must at once within our walls
Bring in the horse.

AEN.　The ropes are ready made
And the wheels are prepar'd
And made fast to its feet.
All the people together
Shall haul the horse along,
To dread Minerva's temple.
Let boys with chaplets crown'd
And choirs of virgins sing,
Sing, dance around
And strew the way with flowers.
The trumpet and the lyre
Shall escort with their music
The horse into Troy.

PRIAM.　Minerva, hear and pardon Troy!

ALL　(*repeat the same words*).

CASS.　Alas! Alas!

All go out. CASSANDRA *is left alone; she starts to follow the crowd, but suddenly turns back.*

CASS.　(*in wild agitation*).
I cannot bear the sight of such rash exultation,
By such blind hopes beguil'd of the day yet to dawn,
The Trojans, doom'd, alas! to fatal destination,
Headlong rush to ruin and destruction.
O remembrance forlorn!
Troy, sacred city built by hands divine!
O valiant heroes of the Trojan line!
Ah, now must I renounce

Ev'ry hope of delight that once I lov'd to
    cherish.
My dream of wedded bliss
Must with him whom I love in Troy's destruction
    perish!
O Choroebus! O my father!
All is now unavailing,
And I relapse unheard in tears and wailing.

*The procession bringing the wooden horse into Troy is
heard very gradually approaching. During the following
scene night falls and at the end of the Act there is complete darkness illuminated only by the torches carried by
the soldiers at the back of the stage.*

PEOPLE (*in the far distance*).
    O thou whom Jove did once engender,
    O thou with spear and buckler girded,
    Virgin and warrior, the gracious and all-wise,
    Pallas, be thou our strong defender,
    Troy by thy shelt'ring pow'r be guarded,
    May we find favour in thine eyes!

CASS.   What is this that I hear?
    Distant voices and music—
    The sacred hymn of Troy—
    What! They come in procession!
    I see them drawing near.

    The enemy comes, and the city receives him.
    There was no need for the King to ordain it,
    For the people themselves have foreseen the
        royal will.

    The holy chant comes louder.

WOMEN. Thy praise let all our song inspire,
    While flutes in consort rising higher
    Pour forth sweet notes of holy strain;

MEN *and* WOMEN. The Phrygian trumpet sets our hearts
      on fire
    The sweeping harp and the Trojan lyre
    Shall fill with music thy tall fane.

CASS. The horse, mounted high upon wheels,
    Is approaching. It is here!

        The chorus comes on to the stage.

PEOPLE. O thou whom Jove, etc.

    Happy children are dancing
    And with garlands advancing
    As tribute gay to bring;
    We strew the way with flowers,
    Like snowy scented showers
    From the realm of the spring.
    Pallas, protect us now!

        The music stops suddenly.

MEN. Why do they stop?

CASS. What is this?

   The people show bewilderment; some women go out as if
   to see what has happened and come back.

MEN. Why is all the convoy in confusion?

CASS. They are waiting, they are all in confusion.

OTHERS. From the bowels of the horse
    Came a clash as of armour—

CASS. They have stopp'd it—ye gods! Ah!

   The people look off-stage, showing signs of anxiety.

MEN. A happy omen! Sing on, sing on!

PEOPLE (*with more enthusiasm than before*).
　　　　From the high towers of Ilium
　　　　Fire shall break forth in triumph,
　　　　And the light of the flame
　　　　Troy victorious shall proclaim!

　　　　The procession, with the wooden horse, passes across the
　　　　stage and disappears into the city.

CASS.　(*as the procession disappears*).
　　　　Stay your hands, stay your hands!
　　　　Bring the fire, bring your axes,
　　　　The hollow sides of the monstrous horse explore!
　　　　Laocoon! He knew
　　　　The snare that the fabric conceals—
　　　　In vain I cry—no one will heed me—
　　　　No mercy have you left, great gods,
　　　　For a nation plung'd in madness.
　　　　Thus, thus does heav'n show its pow'r almighty,
　　　　A whole people to destruction driving
　　　　Down with blinded eyes!

　　　　　She listens to the last notes of the triumphal march.

　　　　They enter—it is done!
　　　　Fate has seiz'd on her prey.
　　　　And I must die, I, Hector's sister,
　　　　Beneath the stones that once were Troy!

　　　　　　　　　　　　　　　　　　　　Exit.

END OF ACT II

ACT III

SCENE 1. *The tent of* AENEAS, *faintly lit by a lamp.* AENEAS, *half clad in armour, lies asleep on his bed.* ASCANIUS *enters, frightened, from the adjoining room; he listens, approaches his father's bed, but does not dare wake him. The noise of fighting, heard before the curtain rises, dies down.*

The GHOST OF HECTOR *appears and advances slowly towards* AENEAS; HECTOR *contemplates* AENEAS *for a moment and sighs deeply.* AENEAS *wakes with a start and sees* HECTOR *standing before him.*

AEN. (*half rising from his bed*).
O thou glory of Troy, O thou light of our
    land!
When we so long have toil'd, thy country to
    defend,
From what region unknown comest thou?
Why are clouded in darkness thine eyes that once
    were clear?
O Hector, why is thy countenance in gloom thus
    enshrouded?

HECT. Aeneas, goddess-born, escape!
The enemy holds our walls,
Troy from its lofty height
In toppling ruin falls!
A hurricane of flame engulfing
With clouds of inky smoke
Our palaces and temples high.
Enough, more than enough,
Have we done for the house of Priam,
All that mortals could do;

15

Troy now entrusts to thee
Her children and her gods.
Go, seek the Latin shore,
And there at last from the ashes of Troy
(Though not ere thou hast wander'd long over
    the waters),
There for the people of Troy risen anew
Thou shalt build up a great and glorious
    empire,
There shalt thou find, like a hero, thy death.

HECTOR *departs with solemnity and his form
gradually becomes more and more indistinct.*

Enter PANTHEUS, *wounded in the face, and carrying
the gods of Troy.*

AEN. What hope is left us yet, Pantheus?
      Whither can we run?
      Where make a stand? What can be done?

PAN. The fire consumes the town, the foe commands.
      The appointed hour is come. Priam is dead,
      And armèd hosts, an unexpected force,
      Break from the bowels of the fatal horse.
      The bold they kill, the unwary they surprise;
      Who fights finds death, and death finds him who
          flies.
      Proud Sinon throws about the flame
      And foes for entrance press without;
      The warders of the gate but scarce maintain
      The unequal combat; they resist in vain.

Enter ASCANIUS.

ASC.   O father!
Ucalegon's palace falls and crashes,
And all the sea is bright with fiery flashes!

AEN.   Come with us, Ascanius!

Enter CHOROEBUS *at the head of an armed force.*

CHOR.   To arms, great Aeneas! Come!
The tower of the citadel yet holds out.

AEN.   We must reach the fort, cost what it may!
Troy calls her sons courageous to defend her;
We will fight to the death, Troy never shall
    surrender!

SOLDIERS. We will fight to the death, Troy never shall
    surrender!
Can you not hear the flames' devouring roar?
The crash of falling tow'r, the shouts of Grecian
    rage?

PAN.   They come, and come yet more—

SOLDIERS. Come on, come on, though gods
No more to Troy assistance lend.
Troy calls her sons courageous to defend her,
We will fight to the death, Troy never shall
    surrender!
Mars and the Furies lead us on,
Mars, lead us on! Die we for Troy!

AENEAS *takes* ASCANIUS *by the hand and places him
in the middle of an armed group.*

17

SCENE 2. *The Temple of Vesta (Cybele); at the back a colon-*
nade with a low parapet, looking towards Mount Ida.
Fire burns on the altar of Vesta; women lie prostrate
in grief before it. The scene is lit by a reddish light from
the burning of the town.
POLYXENA *is among the women.*

WOMEN. O Vesta, be near us,
Great goddess, oh hear us,
Show thy strength and thy power
To those who Troy now are defending,
Thy mighty aid merciful lending,
In this distressful hour!

From the hand of slaughter
Save the wife and daughter
In thy help who trust!
From pollution save us,
Ne'er let foe enslave us
Captive to his lust.

Enter CASSANDRA, *her hair disordered. The con-*
flagration increases; cries of agony are heard far off.

CASS. Not all are doom'd to die.
Aeneas with a handful of warriors,
Three times to the battle returning,
Has now set free those citizens of Troy
Who the high citadel were holding.
And the treasure of the King
Is in their loyal hands.
And soon on the shores of Latium,
Destiny their path directing,
Happier walls, mightier too,
They shall there be erecting.

       There Troy shall rise anew.
       To Ida march they now.

WOMEN. And Choroebus?

CASS.   He is dead.

WOMEN. He is dead!

CASS.   Now do I my last obeisance make
       At the altar of Vesta;
       My bridegroom's fate is mine.
       Life has for me no purpose;
       So let it here be ended!

WOMEN. O prophetess divine!
       Noble daughter of Troy, by the people thought
         demented,
       Had they but heeded thee, yesterday there was
         time;
       They it was that were mad, and have too late
         repented.

CASS.   Yes, now our last hour is at hand.

WOMEN. All is in vain! What shall now be the end?

CASS.   And you, who tremble here in terror,
       What awaits you tonight?
       To be slaves of the conqu'rors!
       Will you accept the plight?
       Vestal virgins, know you the horror,
       The foul desires of brutal might?

WOMEN. Must we abandon the last of our hopes?

CASS.   You must. Hope is a phantom.
       Can you not see, piercing the darkness,
       The fiery glare enveloping the town?
       The clash of arms can you not hear,

And the shouts of Grecian warriors?
They hold the palace gates,
Soon they will seize on our temple!

WOMEN. All is lost, all is lost,
Nothing more can save us now.

CASS.   One thing alone can secure your virgin honour.

(*Pointing to the colonnade above.*)

We may leap to our death
Where steep abyss beneath us yawns.
Why have we else our silken girdles round us?
We need them now, daughters of Troy!

A small group separates from the rest in terror.

WOMEN (*main group*). Thou indeed art a daughter of Troy,
Thy example shall be ours!

CASS.   Will you swear the dawn shall not find you
By Grecian lust polluted?

WOMEN. No, Cassandra, it never shall.

CASS.   Nor ever for their triumph allow them to bind
you?

WOMEN. We swear, and with thee die we all!

The main group take their lyres, play and sing.

Thus faithful to the story
Of our city and fame,
Our death shall cast a shame
On the Grecians' odious glory.
Pure virgins, liv'd we, chaste and free,
To Vesta vow'd eternal;
Virgins and free, descend will we
To shore of the river infernal!

20

CASS. (*to the small group*).
> You that shrink back in silent hesitation,
> Are you afraid?

WOMEN (*small group*). Ah, have we no hope to fly?

CASS. You blench? Are you prepar'd
> For loathsome degradation,
> By Grecian lust defil'd?

WOMEN. Ah me! So young to die!

CASS. Begone!
> To serve the table and the bed of your masters!
> You cowards, shame on you!

WOMEN. Have mercy!

CASS. (*the main group repeat some of her words*).
> Get you gone to your captors,
> Throw yourselves at their feet,
> Suppliant fall at their knees,
> Let them save you! Here you are aliens!
> Shame, shame on you, begone!
> You are no Trojans' daughters!

> *They drive the small group out.*

WOMEN. (*in increasing exaltation*).
> Cassandra, with thee will we die,
> We never will allow these vile Greeks to defile us,
> Or drag us in triumph in chains and revile us.
> No, no, we make our solemn vow.

The conflagration reaches its height. The women take their lyres again and repeat the chorus.

Thus faithful to the story, etc.

CASS. Choroebus! Hector!
      Priam! King, father, brother, belovèd, now
      I come to you! Gods of Hell, hear my vow!

WOMEN. Let the pow'rs who reign below
      Their welcome now prepare us!
      Blow thy horn, Charon, blow,
      O'er the dark waters bear us!

CASSANDRA seizes a lyre and plays. A GREEK
*CHIEFTAIN enters in haste, sword held high, and stops
in astonishment at the sight of the women.*

GREEK Strange sight do I behold!
CHIEF. With the lyre in the hand
      Transported here they sing,
      Though so soon to be captur'd.
      Cassandra, oh how fair is she!
      She leads the band with sapphire eyes aflame,
      By her own song enraptur'd!

Enter some Greek soldiers.

GR. SOL. The treasure! Where's the treasure?
      Hand us over the treasure!

They raise their swords against the women.

CASS. Your threats with scorn we throw back in your
        faces.
      Seek your plunder in vain; you will not find it
        here.
      You are no men of war, but vile robbers and
        thieves.

*She stabs herself with a dagger and hands it to
POLYXENA. POLYXENA stabs herself and falls.*

There! Pain is a thing of naught!

GR. SOL. Furies of Hell! We've lost the plunder!
  Aeneas has escap'd! In the thick of the battle
  Aeneas and his men have fought their bloody way
  With all their gods and gold to freedom!

CASS. (*and* WOMEN). They are free!

WOMEN. To the mountains of Ida now take they their way

  CASSANDRA *tries to reach the colonnade. She falls on one knee.*

  We women stay to face your fury!

  They mount the parapet, draw their daggers and undo their girdles.

  Save Troy her sons, Aeneas!

    They wave their girdles and scarves.

  To Italia! To Italia!

  CASSANDRA *falls dead. Some of the women throw themselves over the parapet, others stab or strangle themselves. The fire has reached the palace, which falls in ruins.*

END OF THE OPERA

THE TROJANS AT CARTHAGE
OPERA IN FOUR ACTS

CHARACTERS
(in the order of their appearance)

DIDO, Queen of Carthage	*Soprano*
ANNA, sister of Dido	*Contralto*
IOPAS, a Tyrian poet	*Tenor*
ASCANIUS, son of Aeneas	*Soprano*
PANTHEUS, a Trojan priest	*Bass*
NARBAL, minister of Dido	*Bass*
AENEAS	*Tenor*
MERCURY	*Bass*
HYLAS, a young Trojan sailor	*Tenor*
FIRST TROJAN SOLDIER	*Baritone*
SECOND TROJAN SOLDIER	*Bass*
GHOST OF PRIAM	*Bass*
GHOST OF CHOROEBUS	*Baritone*
GHOST OF CASSANDRA	*Mezzo-soprano*
GHOST OF HECTOR	*Bass*

Carthaginians, Trojans, Spirits, Nymphs, Fauns, etc.

SCENE. Carthage.

ACT I

SCENE. *A hall of greenery in the palace of* DIDO. *On one side is a throne surrounded by trophies of agriculture, commerce and the arts; on the other, and at the back, an amphitheatre of steps on which an innumerable multitude is seated.*

The first chorus should be sung by the normal opera chorus, the general chorus by the supplementary chorus of men, women and children, placed on the steps along with the opera chorus.

CHORUS OF CARTHAGINIANS.

From a heaven serene favour our gods are show'ring
And gracious bless our festal day;
The tempest that o'er us was low'ring
To shores remote has pass'd away.
The winds breathe soft, and in glorious array
Breaks forth the sun, his gen'rous warmth outpouring,
Life to the earth and strength restoring;
A-tremble with joy, and adoring,
Nature with thankful smile and rapture gay
Salutes his pow'r and kindly ray.
The Queen, the Queen is on her way!

    Enter DIDO *with her train. All rise.*

Hail, all hail to the Queen,
Dido happy and glorious!
In grace and majesty,
In wisdom all-victorious!
Heaven grant her long o'er us to reign,
Rejoicing in the love her subjects bear their Queen!

25

DIDO *takes her seat on the throne, with* ANNA *on her right and* NARBAL *on her left. The people wave palms and scarves, and throw flowers.*

DIDO (*standing*). Seven years are past and gone,
Seven years laborious,
Since we from Tyre sought on the seas a refuge
From the tyrant whose hand my royal spouse had slain,
And to these African shores
Were brought by the favour of heaven.

And already we see our town of Carthage rise.
Duly till'd are our lands, our fleet sails on the sea,
To shores far away, where the first dawn arises,
And they who toil on the waters for us
Bring corn and wine, precious ores too as well,
And products of such arts as to us are unknown.
Proud is your Queen, proud indeed of her nation,
All that you have achiev'd fills my heart with elation;
Yet never stay your hands, let labour ne'er be idle,
The gods will then reveal their secret arts to you,
The forces of nature to bridle,
For conquest ever new.

To all the earth let Carthage stand example,
Mighty in peace, and if war calls to battle,
A nation brave and bold.

ALL.   Mighty in peace, and if war calls to battle,
A nation brave and bold.

DIDO.   I have need of your defence. The swarthy King Iarbas
Would to odious nuptials force my hand.
Never shall he constrain me!

ALL.   Never shall he constrain thee!

DIDO.   Iarbas ne'er on me shall impose his loath'd yoke.
         Our gods' and your protection Dido now must
             invoke.

ALL.   Hail, all hail to the Queen,
         Dido happy and glorious!
         Our lives we gladly give
         That she may be victorious.
         We will her cause defend,
         And the insolent hordes of Iarbas pursuing,
         Beyond the desert's end
         These Numidians we'll chase to rout and to ruin!

DIDO.   Take ye my thanks! All your loyal devotion
         My widow'd bosom thrills with a grateful
             emotion.
         Proceed in strength and pride, and thank the
             gods who gave you
         This home of peace and joy, this kingdom of the
             sea,
         No foe shall e'er enslave you
         Throughout eternal ages be Carthage ever free!

PEOPLE. Her cause we will defend;
         Proceed in strength and pride,
         And thank the gods above us.
         No foe shall e'er enslave us,
         Be Carthage ever free!

DIDO.   By my royal will and pleasure
         This memorable day I have now set apart
         To confer upon all who serve the arts of peace
         The reward of their labours.
         Ye who builded our walls,
         Men of the sea, men of the land,

I bid you now draw near
And receive from me your guerdon,
For it is you whose unremitting toil
Gives to the state its life and strength.

Procession of builders, sailors and labourers to the throne. DIDO *presents a square and an axe to the chief builder; a rudder and an oar to the chief sailor; and a golden sickle to the chief labourer, who is a hale and hearty old man. As she sings the following words she holds in her hands a wreath of flowers and ears of corn.*

Remember!
No man deserves more honour from us all
Than he who tills the ground to feed us.

She crowns the old man with the wreath. Each procession returns to its place after the presentations.

ALL.   Hail the sons of the land!
         Be thankful to them,
         The men of the plough
         And the sowers of grain!

DIDO.   Yes, thank the gods
         That Carthage was not builded in vain!

PEOPLE (*normal opera chorus*).
         Hail, all hail to the Queen,
         Dido happy and glorious!
         Our lives we gladly give
         That she may be victorious.
         Our devotion and love
         That shall never grow cold
         On land and sea
         Shall make us heroes brave and bold.
         Hail to the Queen!

The people, led by NARBAL, *pass before* DIDO *in procession and leave the stage.*

DIDO.   This festal day, these songs of loyal acclamation,

Have brought my troubled heart satisfaction and joy.

Now my soul is at peace; now in safe contemplation

I can face what may come with calm unclouded eye.

ANNA.   Queen of a youthful empire
Rising in wealth and splendour,
Why should your heart be anxious
When you with all are blest?
You, to whose beauty rare
All admiration render,
What mysterious fear
Can find place in your breast?

DIDO.   A mysterious grieving—
Its cause I cannot tell—
Fills my heart with distress.
I resist it in vain;
Oh, it knows no relieving,
My soul with agony is pierc'd,
I feel my bosom heaving,
Till my enfever'd eyes
My burning tears no more repress.

ANNA (*smiling*). It is for love you sigh.

DIDO.   No, that insane emotion
Never again my poor heart shall enslave.

ANNA.   Yet you may love once more.

DIDO. No, in faithful devotion
He who had my vows shall my vows ever have,
For whom I lov'd on earth
I worship in the grave.

ANNA. O Queen, will you so young,
So resplendent in beauty,
Reject the fairest gift
That gods to mortals bring?
For Carthage asks for a King.

DIDO (*pointing to the ring of Sychaeus on her finger*).
May I be of gods and of mortals accursèd
If I should ever be false to my spouse and this
ring!

ANNA. Such hasty vows by heav'n are oft reversèd;
Venus will have her way.
Her will by gods and by men is ever applauded,
And vows like yours in heav'n are not recorded.

DIDO (*aside*). Her voice would in my breast revive
Gleams of a dangerous fire—
A pleasing soft desire—
Mingled with hope unclear,
Though against both in fear
I vainly seek to strive.

ANNA (*aside*). I fain would in her heart revive
Dreams of a fond desire
Of soft unwonted fire,
Her widow'd heart to cheer,
Though against hope her fear
Vainly attempts to strive.

DIDO. O husband whom I lov'd, forgive me!

ANNA. O sister whom I love, forgive me!

DIDO.   If I for one instant to frailty gave way,
        So let thy dear remembrance
        Drive from my heart away
        This thought that will not leave me.

ANNA.   If I have tempted your heart astray;
        But though your secret thoughts
        You fain would hide away,
        Your vows do not deceive me.

Enter IOPAS.

IOPAS. O Queen, a strange fleet has been driv'n on our
        shores;
        Sailors of port unknown have escap'd from the
        tempest,
        And are here to implore an audience at your feet.

DIDO.   To pity the distrest my own suff'rings have
        taught me;
        Go, bid them welcome here.

Exit IOPAS.

        Full well do I recall how I from shore to shore
        Was condemn'd once to wander at the mercy of
        the waters,
        By raging tempest batter'd.
        Full well do I recall the fate I had to ponder,
        When hope was shatter'd!
        I have known storm and stress,
        I have known anxious fear,
        And to those in distress
        How can I be severe?
        They who suppliant before me
        Seek shelter from the stormy main,
        And for mercy implore me,
        Shall never plead their cause in vain.

These fugitives unknown with sudden strange impatience

I await; but a secret apprehension invades me.

DIDO *mounts the throne. Enter* AENEAS, *disguised as a sailor, with* PANTHEUS, ASCANIUS *and the Trojan chieftains carrying gifts.* ASCANIUS *makes obeisance to* DIDO.

ASC. O royal lady, unhappy wanderers are we

Who for a space beg your gracious protection.

At your feet here I lay these few gifts from afar,

The last scattered remains of grandeur now departed,

Which now our pious chief on you would fain confer.

DIDO. And of this chief, noble youth, what is the name and country?

ASC. O lady, with our blood the toilsome path is redden'd

That from the Phrygian mountains leads down to the sea;

That way was ours.

He presents the gifts one by one.

Priam's daughter held this sceptre,

First of her royal line. This diadem was Hecuba's,

And this robe work'd in flow'rs of gold was worn by Helen.

These relics must reveal that our home once was Troy.

DIDO. Was Troy!

ASC. We are led by Aeneas; my father he.

DIDO.   What strange fate brought you hither?

PANTHEUS comes forward.

PAN.   In pious duty to the word of Jove
       Aeneas makes for Italia,
       And on that happy shore he shall meet with his
           end,
       When he has giv'n to us a home, a second
           country.

DIDO.   Great indeed is the fame of noble Hector's
           friend;
       All on his doughty deeds high admiration spend.
       All Carthage knows the story.
       Go, take word to the prince, our harbour shall
           receive
       His fleet,
       And tell him, he and you at my court shall have
           welcome,
       We all your woes will relieve.

Enter NARBAL *in great agitation.*

NAR.   Dreadful news brings me here that my tongue
       scarce can utter!

DIDO.   What is your news?

NAR.   The rebellious Numidian
       Has invaded our land;
       Iarbas himself leads the host,
       'Tis on the way to Carthage.

CHORUS (*in the distance*). Who'll arm us? Who'll arm us?

NAR.   And the wild savage hordes
       Are destroying flocks and herds,
       Laying waste all our fields.
       And more is yet to come;

For Carthage itself is now threaten'd.
Our young warriors are brave,
But how can they defend us?
For we are short of arms.

DIDO.   Can we not save the town?

NAR.   Against such fearful odds
We are bound to go down.

CHORUS (*nearer*). Who'll arm us? Who'll arm us?

AENEAS *throws off his sailor's disguise, and appears in shining armour, but without helmet or shield.*

AEN.   Lady, behold Aeneas!
My ships and men are here by the winds driv'n
for shelter,
Hardy warriors and brave, they to wars are
inur'd;
Troy to you lends her aid, victory then is assur'd.

DIDO.   With pride do I accept your most noble alliance;
United, we may bid defiance,
For now I know the gods are on our side.

(*To* ANNA, *aside*).

Sister, ne'er have I seen such proud and noble
bearing!
Born from goddess of love, her grace and beauty
sharing!

AEN.   On then to war, the black invader to destroy,
We march, twin hosts allied, Carthage and Troy!
As friends in arms united and victorious!
And like the sand before the storm blown away,
To realms consum'd by ever-parching day
The Numidian back we'll drive, inglorious!
Mars, the god Mars to battle calls us.

ALL. Mars, the god Mars to battle calls us,
   Venus's son, great Aeneas, to war leads us on.
   The swarthy hordes shall now be routed,
   From every tow'r then shall be shouted
   The shame of proud Iarbas
   And the triumph we won!

During this chorus the armour of AENEAS *is brought to him and he puts on his helmet and takes shield and spear.*

AEN. (*to* PANTHEUS). Go, tell the men of Troy that Aeneas commands them
   To glorious adventure.

   (*To* DIDO.) Lady, forthwith from your barbarous foe
   You shall find safe deliv'rance.
   And to your loving care I entrust this my son.

DIDO. A mother's love shall enfold him
   In my devoted heart.

AEN. (*to* ASCANIUS). Come, child, embrace thy father!
   Thou wilt perchance from others learn life to enjoy,
   I can teach thee only how to become a hero
   And heaven's will obey.
   Hold thy heart brave and true, nor e'er forget the story
   Of Aeneas and of Hector, thy ensamples of glory!

The people of Carthage enter from all sides, demanding arms. Only a few men carry regular arms; the rest have scythes, axes and slings.

CHORUS. Who'll arm us? Who'll arm us?

ALL.   On then to war, the black invader to destroy!
We march, twin hosts allied, Carthage and Troy!
As friends in arms united and victorious.
And like the sand before the storm blown away,
To realms of ever-parching day
The Numidian back we'll drive inglorious!
Mars, the god Mars, etc.

END OF ACT I

ACT II

SCENE 1. *Garden of* DIDO, *on the sea-shore, decorated with wreaths to celebrate the return of* AENEAS *after defeating Iarbas.*

ANNA *and* NARBAL *are discovered.*

ANNA.   Tell me, I pray, what cause have you for fearing?
The war is over and its horrors at an end.
Our warriors have return'd, the spoils of triumph
    bearing,
Are we not safe? What danger can portend?

NAR.   From war Carthage is safe, no invader need alarm
    us;
The Numidians are fled; they have no pow'r to
    harm us;
They never more will dare to approach our
    walls.
By the sword of Aeneas, that invincible hero,
Their King was doom'd to fall.
Danger lurks here within.
Our Queen neglects the cares that once to her
    were dear.
In feasting, or the chase, all her days now she
    passes;
All labour's at an end, our people toil no
    more.
Far too long is the Trojan in Carthage remaining,
And I am not alone in my anxious complaining.

ANNA.   You surely must already see that she loves him,
This warrior proud; can you not see that he too
For the Queen burns with equal flame?

37

NAR.   What!

ANNA.   Why should you be apprehensive
If their hearts beat the same?
For Dido, who could be a more heroic spouse?
For Carthage, who a more illustrious king?

NAR.   The summons of inexorable Fate
Calls this Aeneas to Italia.

ANNA.   One voice to him says 'Go!'
Another voice is crying 'Stay!'
The greatest of all the gods is Love.

NAR.   What awful doom for Carthage art thou holding,
Future obscure, soon down on us to crash?
The thunderbolt and the lightning-flash
Break forth from thy cloud enfolding.
Jupiter, thou who to man hast ordain'd
That he should welcome and succour the
stranger,
Have we deserv'd, for the deed of a friend,
That thou shouldst smite us in anger?

ANNA.   Why should you fear?
Our Carthage is victorious;
Dido the Queen all-glorious
Loves her defender dear.

Cupid's train of Loves and Graces
Both with flowery chain enlaces,
And that is the menace of your future obscure.

Enter DIDO *and* AENEAS, *with* ASCANIUS, IOPAS *and*
court. ASCANIUS *takes the arms of* AENEAS *and hangs*
them up in the temple of Minerva.
Ballet and chorus of Nubian slaves.

38

NUB. SL. A ma loué mi-donaé
   Fai cara imé
   Dei bera imbé.
   Ha!

   After the ballet DIDO *comes down from the throne and
   lies down on a couch at the front of the stage. At a sign
   from* ANNA *the dancers go away.*

DIDO (*languidly*). An end, I pray, I am weary of dances,
   I am weary of feasting.

   AENEAS *stands before* DIDO.

   Iopas prithee sing,
   I am in mood for music now,
   For simple song and sweet.

IOPAS. The Queen deigns to command me, I obey.

   A Theban harpist comes forward and accompanies
   IOPAS.

   O Ceres, goddess fair,
   When thy kindly care
   On young seed that groweth
   The first green blade bestoweth,
   Take our grateful prayer.

   The men of the field
   Thank thee for the yield,
   Gratefully receiving
   Thy promise of giving
   The corn in the ear.

   Ev'ry soaring bird,
   Ev'ry lamb of the herd,
   Each wind that bloweth
   And a perfume stroweth,
   Thy endless bounty share.

> For the gifts we share
> Of the balmy air
> And the ripening ear
> Take our grateful prayer!

DIDO. I pray you forgive me, Iopas,
Not even your sweet voice can charm me,
I cannot listen any more.

*AENEAS sits at the feet of DIDO. ASCANIUS, leaning
on his bow and looking like a statue of Cupid, stands
on DIDO's left. ANNA leans with her elbow on the back
of the couch. NARBAL and IOPAS stand near ANNA.*

AEN. Belovèd Queen!

DIDO. Aeneas! Oh, relate to the end
The woeful tale of Troy, your wand'rings on the
seas.
I never tire to hearken.
Andromache the fair, what was her later fortune?

AEN. Alas! She to Epirus
In slavery was led. She begg'd in vain to die,
But Pyrrhus the King so distractedly lov'd her,
That at last her heart laid aside
All remembrance of Troy, and after long refusal
To Pyrrhus she was wed.

DIDO. She that was Hector's wife!

AEN. She that was Hector's wife,
She now is Queen of Epirus.

DIDO. Oh, for shame!
(*Aside.*) All conspires
To vanquish my remorse, and my heart to absolve.
Hector's wife has espous'd him who murder'd
her father,

The son of him that slew her husband Hector
    himself!

AEN.   Her conqu'ror she adores, though her father he
    murder'd,
    Though son of him that slew her husband
    Hector himself.

DIDO *puts her arm round the neck of* ASCANIUS *so that
her hand falls over his shoulder. He smilingly takes the
ring of Sychaeus from her finger;* DIDO *takes it from
him absent-mindedly, and lets it fall on the couch when
she rises.*

DIDO.   All conspires, etc.

ANNA (*to* NARBAL). Do you remark the boy Ascanius,
    How like a little Cupid he appears?
    From Dido's hand he gently tears
    The ring of dead Sychaeus.

        IOPAS *and* NARBAL *repeat the same words.*

AEN.   All conspires to vanquish her remorse, etc.

Oh talk no more of past memories of sadness!
(*Rising.*) Behold this night of splendour!
A cool breeze fans the air with a tender caress;
Dido, arise and taste its fragrance!

               DIDO *rises.*

ASCANIUS, DIDO, ANNA, AENEAS, IOPAS, NARBAL, PANTHEUS.
Night throws her veil of enchantment all around,
In peace all things enfolding, while far away the
    ocean,
To sleep lulling the waves, makes a soft mur-
    m'ring sound.

All except DIDO *and* AENEAS *retire towards the back
and disappear.*

DIDO *and* AEN. O sweet night, night of ecstasy unending!
>> O goddess bright, Diana thron'd above!
>> Pour out on us thy blessèd ray with starlight
>> blending,
>> Flow'rs of heav'n, oh smile on our immortal
>> love!

DIDO. In such a night as this the Queen of Loves and
>> Graces,
>> Your mother Venus, found Anchises' warm
>> embraces,
>> Under Ida's deep shade.

AEN. In such a night as this, mad with love and with
>> joy,
>> Troilus once awaited under the walls of Troy
>> Cressid the lovely maid.

BOTH. O sweet night, etc.

AEN. In such a night as this, ere the starlight was paling,
>> Diana stepp'd to earth, her fair body unveiling
>> In young Endymion's arms.

DIDO. In such a night as this the son whom Venus bore
>> Was cold to the love that a queen did outpour,
>> Found in Dido no charms.

AEN. That night, that very night, unjustly him accusing,
>> She receiv'd from his lips—how could they be
>> refusing?
>> Pledge that sooth'd her alarms.

BOTH. O sweet night, etc.

>> *They move slowly towards the back in an embrace.*
>> DIDO *leans on* AENEAS'S *shoulder; they depart slowly.*
>> *Suddenly* MERCURY *appears in a ray of moonlight near*
>> *a broken column on which the arms of* AENEAS *are*

hung. He draws near to the column and strikes two blows on the shield, which rings with a prolonged melancholy sound.

MER.   To Italia! To Italia! To Italia!

MERCURY *vanishes.*

SYMPHONIC ENTR'ACTE—THE ROYAL HUNT

SCENE 2. *A virgin forest near Carthage. Morning. At the back is a very high rock, with the entrance to a cave at the foot on the left. A little stream runs along the rock and runs into a natural basin bordered with reeds and rushes.*

NAIADS *appear; two are just visible behind the rushes and then vanish. The* NAIADS *are seen swimming in the basin.*

The Royal Hunt. Horns are heard in the forest far away. The NAIADS *listen anxiously and look in the direction of the sound. They move towards the right wings with increasing anxiety, finally disappearing among the reeds. Hunters pass across the stage. Then a single hunter passes; he seems afraid of the approaching storm. Then he leaves his shelter and goes off in the direction of the horns. It grows dark, and rain falls.*

ASCANIUS *gallops across the stage on horseback, followed by other hunters on horseback, at some distance. Other hunters appear on foot, flying in all directions.*

DIDO *and* AENEAS *enter battling against the storm. It is now almost night.* DIDO *is dressed as the huntress Diana, a bow in her hand and a quiver on her shoulder.* AENEAS *is in semi-military costume.* DIDO *and* AENEAS *go into the cave.*

43

> *Wood-nymphs appear on the top of the rock; they move excitedly about the stage with wild gestures.*

NYMPHS. A-o a-o a-o a-o a-o!

> FAUNS *enter, dancing. The stream becomes larger and makes a roaring waterfall.*

NYMPHS, FAUNS, *etc.* To Italia! To Italia!

> *More waterfalls rise out of the rock, increasing the noise of the storm. Satyrs and Sylvans perform grotesque dances in the darkness.*
>
> *Lightning strikes a tree, breaks it and sets it on fire; the remains of it fall on the stage. The Fauns and Sylvans seize flaming branches and dance holding them in their hands.*

NYMPHS, FAUNS, *etc.* O-a o-a o-a O!

> *They all rush away. The stage gradually becomes covered with thick clouds, till it is entirely hidden. The storm dies down. The clouds rise and disappear.*

END OF ACT II

ACT III

SCENE. *The harbour, with Trojan tents on the shore and the
    Trojan ships anchored. It is night.*
    *A young sailor sings at the masthead of a ship. Two
    sentries are on guard by the tents at the back.*

HYLAS (*the young sailor*).

> O vale resounding
> Whose woods surrounding
> The cry did once prolong,
> Alas!
> Shall ever I those echoes set rebounding
> With cheerful song?
>
> Rock me gently then, on thy bosom leaning,
> Mighty mother sea, and comfort my complaining!
>
> Pine-trees and larches
> Of Ida's marches,
> Cool and refreshing glade,
> Alas!
> When shall I breathe the scent of your green arches,
> When find your shade?
>
> Rock me gently then, on thy bosom leaning,
> Mighty mother sea, and comfort my complaining!
>
> Mother who bore me,
> Who will restore me
> To thy long-lost embrace?
> Alas!
> Shall I in dreams alone behold before me
> Thy tender face?
>
> Rock me gently then, on thy bosom leaning,
> Mighty mother sea, and comfort my complaining!

1ST SENTRY. He's dreaming of his home—

2ND SENT. Which he'll ne'er see again.

        Enter PANTHEUS *and Trojan chieftains.*

PAN.   The time has come; we must prepare to sail.
        With vain despair Aeneas now beholds
        The agony of Dido; but he has heard the call
        Of duty and of glory.
        And his heart will be firm in the hour of
           farewell.

PAN. *and* CHIEFS. We have stirr'd up the wrath of the gods
          by delay!
        They warn us of our sin with many a sign and
          wonder.
        With shrieks and groans the earth is rent
          asunder,
        By unseen hands our arms are clash'd with
          noise like thunder,
        As once in Troy, on that disastrous night,
        The ghost of Hector in anger appear'd before
          our sight,
        All the host of the dead to reproach us draw
          nigh,
        Last night again they hail'd us with threefold
          cry—

GHOSTS (*invisible*). To Italia! To Italia! To Italia!

PAN. *and* CHIEFS. We are warn'd! We must fly!
        Jove's command all too long have we now
          disregarded;
        Let our departure hence be no longer retarded!
        Hence, away!
        We must depart this day.

They go into their tents. Two SENTRIES *march across the stage, two steps to a bar of music; one goes from right to left, the other from left to right. From time to time they stand still together in the middle of the stage.*

1ST SENT. Say, good friend, why this haste
To sail away from Carthage?
I know not what they mean.

2ND SENT. Nor I.

1ST SENT. More easy quarters
Than these I've never seen.

2ND SENT. Why would they bid us go,
When we can eat our fill
And wash it down with wine?

1ST SENT. I talk right pretty Carthaginian
To all the merry wantons of the place.

2ND SENT. These wenches are just to my taste,
Buxom and gay, that is my opinion.

1ST SENT. They'll soon learn the language of Troy.

2ND SENT. Trojan soldiers know how to win them.
These wenches all are kind
To men from foreign parts.

BOTH. Ay, for all are well inclin'd
To take us to their hearts.

1ST SENT. And why should we be forc'd to leave
This gay life and go again a-sailing?

2ND SENT. To hear the winds about us wailing!

1ST SENT. A life at sea is a life accurst.

2ND SENT. Plague and sickness, hunger and thirst.

1ST SENT. And where are we going?

2ND SENT. Faith, that there's no knowing.

1ST SENT. And what will be our life
    If e'er we come ashore?

2ND SENT. They'll only make us toil the more.

BOTH.   For what are we?

1ST SENT. We are slaves, chattels of our masters.

2ND SENT. Be silent! Aeneas comes.
    We are in for disasters.

Exeunt SENTRIES. *Enter* AENEAS *in great agitation.*

AEN.   There is no turning back; this land I must
       relinquish.
    The Queen knows all; her alarm, when she heard
    My fix'd intent, my resolve would extinguish.
    No! Duty calls, I must go.

    How can I ever forget how she pal'd,
    With looks distraught by mortal anguish!
    Ne'er a word would she speak; her eyes
    Blaz'd with a fire dark and sombre.
    In vain told I of portents and signs without
       number
    Warning me hence to high emprise,
    Spoke in vain of my life to this call consecrated,
    Of my hopes for my son and the children of Troy,
    And of the glorious death which unto me is fated,
    Death on the Latin field, to crown my life with
       joy;
    No words will move her heart; her silence ne'er
       was broken.
    I fled before that glance of eloquence unspoken.
    How dare I face the hour when for aye we must
       part,

Hour of despair and of anguish unending?
How dare I leave that tortur'd heart
Which pangs of grief and rage are rending?
Can I coldly renounce thee, O Queen whom I
    adore,
And when I pierce thy soul, thy forgiveness
    implore?
'Twere the deed of a traitor! And am I not
    Aeneas?

May storm and tempest rack me,
Drown me deep in the main,
If I, ere I quit Carthage,
See thee not once again!

Leave thee thus? Oh, 'twere vile!
Can I this house of shelter ungrateful thus defile?
Ah no! Thou Queen belovèd,
Thou soul sublime that by my act wast bruisèd,
Thou protectress of Troy,
Nay, I will see thee again,
To press thy trembling hands, for the last time
    returning,
To pour out on thy knees my tears of anguish
    burning,
Though crush'd indeed were I under thy load of
    pain!

GHOSTS (*invisible*). Aeneas!

AEN.   That voice again!

    The ghost of PRIAM *appears in the wings, veiled, on the
    spectators' right.*

                 Thou messenger of Hades,
From the realm of the dead, what brings thee
    here to me?

PRIAM (*visible*). Hast thou forgot thy glory?

AEN.   Ah! Would that I could die!

PRIAM.   No more delay!

GHOST OF CHOROEBUS (*invisible*). Not a day!

GHOSTS OF CASSANDRA *and* HECTOR (*invisible*). Not an hour.

PRIAM (*unveiling before the eyes of* AENEAS). Priam am I

> Thou must live and be gone.   PRIAM *vanishes.*
>
> AENEAS, *rushing madly towards the right, meets the ghost of* CHOROEBUS, *veiled, appearing in the wings.* CHOROEBUS *unveils before his eyes.*

CHOR.   I am Choroebus!
> Thou must go hence to conquer!

> > CHOROEBUS *vanishes.*

> AENEAS, *starting back towards the back of the stage, meets the other two ghosts, recognizing them when they unveil.* CASSANDRA *leans with her left arm on* HECTOR's *shoulder.* HECTOR *is in full armour.*

AEN.   Hector! Ye gods of Hades! Cassandra!

CASS. *and* HECT. Thou must build Troy anew!

> > *They vanish.*

AEN.   I yield, I yield to your pitiless commandment,
I obey, I obey, ye shades of Troy prophetic!
If I must cruel be, it is the gods' command.
Dido a sacrifice must fall by my unseeing hand.

> > AENEAS *passes before the tents.*

> Awake, awake! Trojans, awake from slumber!
> Shake off the sleep, your eyes that doth encumber,
> Trojans, awake, put out to sea!
> For we must sail or ever the sun shall arise.

TROJANS. Bestir ye! Bestir ye!
   Do ye not hear the call of great Aeneas?
   Bestir ye! Bestir ye!
   And let no Trojan in sleep close his eyes.

AEN. (*to a chieftain*). Go, go, haste thee at once to the tent
   of the prince
   Ascanius; he must rise and come at once on board.
   Before the dawn we must be far at sea.
   My task up to the end, great gods, shall be per-
   formèd.
   Arouse ye, men! Not a moment's delay!
   Cut ye the cables, it is time, to sea, to sea!
   For Italia! For Italia!

TROJANS. Soon 'twill be day, not a moment's delay,
   Cut we the cables, it is time, to sea, to sea!
   For Italia! For Italia!

   *They rush off the stage in various directions. The ships
   are seen beginning to move.*

AEN. (*looking towards* DIDO's *palace*).
   Belovèd Dido, farewell! Thy pardon I deserve,
   Though haste I must away.
   My destiny impatient calls me,
   As a hero to die. I to thee must be faithless.

        Distant lightning and thunder.

     DIDO *enters precipitately.*

DIDO. Thy footsteps I pursue mid the lightning and
   thunder,
   Can it be true? Indeed, I see but cannot believe—
   You prepare now to fly me?

AEN. My heart is torn asunder.
   Dido, belov'd, spare me, oh, spare!

DIDO.   You go? Can you dare?
        Dar'st thou, the crown of Carthage thus re-
            jecting,
        Disdain my love, thy steps to Latin shore
            directing?

AEN.   Alas, too long I brav'd the high command of
            Jove.

DIDO.   He goes! This voice divine must so compelling
            prove
        That it can mine ignore? To his cruel disdain
        He can let me lay bare my unspeakable torment,

        *She notices a group of Trojans looking at her and
        smiling.*

        My royal beauty rare
        To the laughter and the scorn of his ungrateful
            men?

AEN.   No, no!

DIDO.   Nor can the sight of such anguish appalling
        One poor pitiful tear from those hard eyes set
            falling?
        Hewn from the harden'd entrails of a rock,
        'Twas rough Hyrcanian tigers gave thee suck.

AEN.   O Dido, when for thee my heart first knew desire,
        It yielded to the law of love's immortal pow'r,
        And to my dying hour
        Thy love will all my soul inspire.

DIDO.   No more! Nothing will move thee,
        Not e'en the death that hangs above me,
        My shame, nor all my love, nor our first nuptial
            embrace,
        Nor all that that has caus'd me of open disgrace!

Yet had you left behind some pledge of our
    delight,

Yes, if some young Aeneas could bless the
    mother's sight,

Could smile upon my heart and your features
    recall,

I had not wholly lost a husband.

AEN.   Oh, forgive me, forgive ! Dido, I love thee!
Great Jove alone by his mighty command
Could induce me to leave thee.

                 The sound of the Trojan march is heard.

DIDO.   At the sound of that song that shall lead thee to
    glory
I see thy soul enthrall'd! You go?

AEN.   Yes, go I must.

DIDO.   You go?

AEN.   And to my death. The gods I must obey.
I go. Dido, I love thee.

DIDO.   Get thee hence, get thee gone, let me see thee no
    more!
False, cruel and forsworn! Begone! Hence!
May thyself and thy gods be accursèd!

                                  Exit.
Groups of Trojan soldiers pass preparing for departure.

SAILORS. For Italia! For Italia!

ASCANIUS *enters, escorted by a Trojan chieftain.*
AENEAS, *who has remained motionless for a time, is
stirred to action by the shouts of his men and goes on
board a ship.*

AEN. *and* MEN. For Italia!

END OF ACT III

ACT IV

SCENE 1. *A room in* DIDO's *palace*. DIDO *and* ANNA *are discovered*.

DIDO.   Haste, seek him, my haughty foe,
Tell him, I will abase me.
My pride is dead. Go! His departure slays me.
I know too well he will not stay.

ANNA.   I blame myself for this misfortune.
That I to this alliance your heart did persuade.
The will of heav'n none can evade;
He will go, nothing can restrain him,
Yet he loves you, and you alone.

DIDO.   He loves me? No! No! His heart is of stone.
Love cannot be denied; should all the gods in
heaven
Against my love conspire, I the gods would defy,
The awful curse of Jove himself braving!
Yet, sister, go, go, Narbal too, him to entreat
That he at least would grant me but a few days of
delay.
Humbly I do beseech him.
All I for him have done can he now thus forget?
Oh, how can he refuse this entreaty despairing
That you, counsellor wise, and sister dear, are
bearing?

VOICES (*far off*). To sea they go!
Vessels five, seven, nine, ten!

Enter IOPAS.

IOPAS.   The Trojan fleet is gone!

DIDO.   Oh, horror!

IOPAS. Before the dawn their ships put out to sea;
They are not out of sight yet.

DIDO. What shall I do? He's gone!
Carthaginians, to arms! Haste, haul my galleys out!
Pursue the perjur'd foe, to follow, sink and burn them!
Bring flaming brands, set sail and swiftly row!
Let him never escape that dar'd to betray me!
Where am I? Fury turns my brain.
To fate's decree I must submit me,
Devour my grief alone—O wretched Dido!
Behold the promis'd faith of this pious Aeneas!
A throne I offer'd! Ah, had I only known,
I should have torn this wand'ring race of Trojans
Limb from limb, and cast their mangled corpses
To perish in the sea!
Had I then all their faithless perfidy foreseen,
Their fleet destroy'd by fire had been,
Last vengeance on Aeneas, I for a hideous feast
The flesh of his own son had serv'd for him to taste!

To Hell now must I pray; Olympus will not hear me.
Hear my cry, hear my cry, ye dark pow'rs and dread!
Teach my hatred to curse him,
Traitor to Dido's throne and bed!

Go, send for Pluto's priest; I have need of his service.
His rites alone my torment can relieve.

Forthwith prepare a sacrifice to offer
To all the gloomy pow'rs in the realms of the
grave.
Raise a funeral pyre! Bring the gifts that he gave
me,
And those I gave to him; to the flames I consign
them.
Perish thus ev'ry hated memorial! Now leave me.

NAR. (*aside to* ANNA).

The Queen's looks are wild; leave her not, I
beseech.

DIDO.   Sister, I bid you go.

ANNA.   You desire me to leave you?

DIDO.   I am your Queen, I command you; leave me
alone, I say.

Exeunt ANNA, IOPAS *and* NARBAL.

DIDO *crosses the stage, tearing her hair, beating her
breast and uttering inarticulate cries.*

Ah! Ah!

She stops suddenly.

Now must I die.
My grief is past endurance; it o'erwhelms me.
And I die unreveng'd! A double death.
Oh, when from far away
He sees the livid flame rise from the funeral pyre
for me,
If still within his soul there be yet one human
thought,
Perchance one tear he'll weep for Dido's hapless
lot,
One kindly tear! Aeneas, yes, I am thy slave,

And to thy love for ever fetter'd,
Thy slave am I, and bear it with me beyond the
grave.
O Venus, give me back thy son!
To what purpose is praying,
When hope is lost for ever?
Only death now can hear me, and I am vow'd to
death;
Now must I die.

Farewell, Carthage of mine, proud city that I
rais'd,
Thou of my reign memorial abiding,
Thou, sister, farewell, thou all my wand'ring life
with me dividing.
Farewell, my people all,
Farewell, thou hospitable shore,
Where first my ships found rest at anchor riding.
Farewell, thou starry sky, I shall see thee no more,
Thy ardent blaze to my passion's ecstasy lending,
I shall see thee no more; now must death be the
ending.

SCENE 2. *A terrace overlooking the sea.*
> *The priests of Pluto enter in procession and group
> themselves near two altars on which burn greenish
> flames.*
> DIDO *is covered with a veil and crowned with leaves.*
> ANNA *unlooses* DIDO's *hair and takes off her left shoe
> (ritual of sacrifice to the infernal deities).*

PRIESTS. Tartarus, hear, Orcus and Chaos,
Peace to this wounded heart and new strength
restore!

Hear, threefold Hecate and Erebus,
Hear us, ye powers infernal whom nameless we
implore!

ANNA *and* NARBAL (*stretching out their right hands towards the
sea*). The horrid curse of Hell fall now on false
Aeneas,

May he find ignominious death!
May ev'ry Latin tribe its forces join against him,
So to obstruct his path!
By spear unknown laid low, in bloody battle
falling,
May he be left to bleed 'mid the carnage appalling,
Till foul vultures devouring end his life of shame!
Hear us, ye pow'rs infernal, ye gods we dare not
name!

DIDO, *with slow and irregular steps, walks twice round
the funeral pyre during the last part of this chorus.*

ANNA, NARBAL *and* PRIESTS. Tartarus, hear, etc.

DIDO (*speaking as if in a dream*).

The gods of Hades seem to be propitious,
Now in this hour unblest.
O Narbal, O sister, all is done;
Yet but remains the sacrifice to finish,
And then at last my bosom is at rest.

*Two priests, carrying the first altar, move from left to
right; two others, carrying the second altar, move from
right to left. They cross and make the round of the pyre.*
DIDO, *her left foot bare and her hair loose, lays down
her crown on leaves on one of the altars, and follows the
altar with halting steps.*
*The high priest of Pluto, standing, stretches out the
Plutonic pitchfork towards the pyre.*

DIDO *quickly mounts the steps of the pyre. When she is at the top, she takes the toga of* AENEAS, *removes the gold-embroidered veil from her head and throws them both on the pyre.*

DIDO. Of my unhappy love let these the pledges
Be consum'd in the flames with my grief and my hate.

She contemplates the armour of AENEAS, *and sighs. She throws herself on the bed, which she kisses with convulsive sobs. Then she rises, takes the sword, and speaks in prophetic tones.*

The memory of me shall live throughout the ages,
My people shall fulfil a great and glorious fate.
One day, in this kingdom of Carthage,
From my ashes shall arise the avenger of my shame,
Ev'n now I hear the thunder of his name—
Hannibal! Hannibal! With pride my bosom swelleth,
All forgotten is my woe,
Now like a queen I die, glorious among the ghosts below.

She draws the sword from the scabbard, stabs herself and falls on the bed.

ANNA, NARBAL *and* PRIESTS. Ah! Help the Queen!
By her own hand she's dying!

NARBAL *goes out for help and returns with a crowd of people, courtiers and attendants.*

PEOPLE. The Queen! Help the Queen!
In her own blood lying!
O fatal sight! O horror! Day of woe!
The Queen! She dies!

DIDO (*rising on her elbow*). Ah!

ANNA (*on the pyre*). Sister, 'tis I,
    'Tis thy sister who calls thee.

DIDO (*half rising*). Unrelenting in hate, our destiny I fore-
        see.
        Carthage for ever doom'd,
        Roma, Roma, (*Standing.*) City Eternal!

*A vision appears in a halo at the back—the Roman
Capitol; on the façade in shining letters the word* ROMA.
DIDO *falls and dies.* ANNA *falls swooning beside her.*
*In front of the Capitol are seen grouped legions,
artists and poets surrounding a proconsul.*
*The Carthaginians move to the front of the stage
with their backs to the pyre.*

PEOPLE. Vengeance we swear on the race of the Trojan,
        Hatred and war to our enemy mortal.
        And our children of ev'ry generation to come
        Our foe shall still pursue!
        Our ships shall assail them at sea,
        And by land too as well as by water
        The war we will renew!
        A future age shall see the sons of Carthage arise
        To massacre these Romans
        And extirpate their brood in an orgy of slaughter!

END OF THE OPERA